THE WONDERFUL

DAHLOV IPCAR

EGG

DOUBLEDAY & COMPANY, INC.,

GARDEN CITY, NEW YORK

81 6293 5

49

For Bobby, who wanted Dinosaur pictures

In the back of this book
you will find a chart that
tells how big the dinosaurs
were, and a page that tells
you how to say their names.

Long, long ago, more than one hundred million years ago, everything was different than it is today. It was so long ago that there were no cities or houses or even people. All the earth was covered with big green jungles. They were hot, damp, tangled jungles of huge moss trees and giant fern trees, for even the trees were different then.

Back in those long-ago times the only animals that lived in the green jungles of the world were the dinosaurs. They were very strange beasts and most of them were big. Stupendously, tremendously, enormously BIG.

They trampled through the green jungles on their big feet, and they waded
through the swamps. Other huge reptiles swam in the warm seas. Some even
flew through the air on big leather bat wings. And they all laid eggs.

And one wonderful egg sat all alone in a blue-green mossy nest at the base of a giant fern tree in the green jungle world.

Was it a dinosaur egg? Did a mother dinosaur lay that egg to hatch into a baby dinosaur? All the dinosaurs hatched from eggs, so it might be a dinosaur egg.

Was it a Brontosaurus egg? Brontosaurus was a really ENORMOUS dinosaur.
The huge "Thunder-Lizard." He had a great heavy body on thick legs like tree
trunks, a long trailing tail, and a long snake-like neck with a little head like
a salamander's head, looking this way and that, swaying along, wading
through the green marshy swamps of long ago.

Was it a Triceratops egg? Triceratops was big too, but
not as big as Brontosaurus. He had two big horns over
his eyes and another horn on his hooked beak of a nose,
and he had a big bony frill around his neck. There were
several kinds of big dinosaurs with horns and frills, but
Triceratops was the biggest.

Or was it a Stegosaurus egg? Stegosaurus was big too.
He had rows of high bony plates that ran up and down
his back like a fence all the way to the tip of his long
tail, and at the end of his tail he had four big spikes.

Pteranodon was a huge flying reptile with great wings like a bat, more than twenty feet across from tip to tip. He flew high over the green tree tops on his big flapping wings. Perhaps it was a Pteranodon egg?

Maybe it was an Ornithomimus egg? Ornithomimus, the "ostrich" dinosaur, was timid, and he could run very fast. He had a beak like a bird's and a long neck, and he walked on his hind legs. He looked almost like a long-tailed featherless ostrich.

Or was it an Elasmosaurus egg? Elasmosaurus was one of the big reptiles that lived in the deep seas of long ago. He was one of the biggest, sometimes measuring forty feet from the tip of his nose to the tip of his tail. He swam and dived in the water and had four flippers like a seal, but he had a long neck like a snake, and a short snake-like tail.

Could it be a Tyrannosaurus egg? Tyrannosaurus was the largest of the big hunting dinosaurs. He was very ferocious, with terrible teeth, and he hunted and ate other dinosaurs. He walked upright on his strong heavy hind legs, and the earth shook under him as he stalked through the jungles on his big clawed feet looking for his prey.

Trachodon was another big dinosaur that walked on his hind legs, but he was gentle and peaceful and ate plants. He had a narrow flat head with a nose shaped like a duck's bill. He lived in the swamplands, where he splashed in the mud and swam in the water. Perhaps it was a Trachodon egg?

Or was it a Corythosaurus egg? Corythosaurus was another duck-billed dinosaur that liked to swim and wade in the swamps. He was the "helmet-crested" duck-bill.

Parasaurolophus was duck-billed too, but with a different kind of crest on his head. Could it be a Parasaurolophus egg?

Tylosaurus was another big reptile that lived in the
warm seas. He had four flippers, and perhaps a wavy
fin down his back and along his tail. And he had a big
mouth full of sharp teeth for catching fish. Was it a
Tylosaurus egg?

Or could it be an Ankylosaurus egg? Ankylosaurus was a medium-sized dinosaur with thick armor-like plates of bone all over his back and big spikes sticking out all along his sides.

But no, it wasn't a dinosaur egg at all.

It was a wonderful new kind of egg.

And when it hatched, it hatched into a baby bird, the first baby bird in the whole world. And the baby bird grew up to be a beautiful bird with feathers. The first beautiful bird that ever sang a song high in the tree tops of the new green world of long, long ago.

THIS IS HOW BIG THEY WERE

scale ⅛ inch = 1 foot

Brontosaurus   70 feet long

Trachodon   30 feet long

Corythosaurus   30 feet long

Parasaurolophus   30 feet lon

Triceratops   25 feet long

Stegosaurus   20 feet long

Tyrannosaurus   50 feet long

Elasmosaurus   40 feet long

Tylosaurus   30 feet long

Pteranodon   25 foot wingspread

Rhamphorhynchus
(small flying reptile)

Archaeopteryx
(the first bird)

Both chicken size

Orinthomimus   12 feet long

Ankylosaurus   10 feet long

THIS IS THE WAY TO SAY THEIR NAMES

Ankylosaurus   AN-kill-o-sawr-us

Archaeopteryx   ark-e-OP-ter-ix

Brontosaurus   BRON-toe-sawr-us

Corythosaurus   cor-ITH-o-sawr-us

Elasmosaurus   ee-LAZ-mo-sawr-us

Ornithomimus   orn-i-tho-MYME-us

Parasaurolophus   pear-a-sawr-OL-o-fus

Pteranodon   tare-AN-o-don

Rhamphorhynchus   ram-fo-RINK-us

Stegosaurus   STEG-o-sawr-us

Trachodon   TRACK-o-don

Triceratops   try-SER-a-tops

Tylosaurus   TILE-o-sawr-us

Tyrannosaurus   tie-RAN-o-sawr-us

Rhamphorhynchus

Archaeopteryx